Preface

Upon instruction by the Maritime Safety Committee (MSC) the Sub-Committee on Containers and Cargoes developed the first Code of Safe Practice for Ships Carrying Timber Deck Cargoes in the early 1970s. The Code was approved by the MSC at its twenty-fifth session (March 1972) and adopted by the Assembly at its eighth regular session (November 1973) by resolution A.287(VIII).

The Assembly recommended that Governments implement the Code and authorized the MSC to keep the Code up to date by adopting such amendments as might be necessary.

Recognizing the need to improve the provisions contained in the Code in light of experience gained, the Sub-Committee on Containers and Cargoes subsequently revised the Code. The MSC approved the revised Code at its fifty-eighth session (May 1990) and the Assembly, at its seventeenth regular session (November 1991), adopted it by resolution A.715(17), which revoked resolution A.287(VIII).

The revised Code is contained in the present edition. Any amendments or further revisions which may be made will be included in subsequent editions of the Code.

Contents

Page

Foreword   1

Chapter 1   – General   1

Chapter 2   – Stability   2

Chapter 3   – Stowage   3

Chapter 4   – Securing   5

Chapter 5   – Personnel protection and safety devices   8

Chapter 6   – Action to be taken during the voyage   9

Appendix A   – Advice on stowage practices   11

Appendix B   – General guidelines for the under-deck
                stowage of logs   22

Appendix C   – Recommendation on intact stability
                for passenger and cargo ships under
                100 m in length, as amended, with
                respect to ships carrying deck cargoes   25

                Appendix 1 – Calculation of stability
                               curves   29

                Appendix 2 – Standard conditions of
                               loading to be examined   33

                Appendix 3 – Memorandum to Administra-
                               tions on an approximate
                               determination of ship's
                               stability by means of
                               the rolling period tests
                               (for ships up to 70 m
                               in length)   35

                Annex – Suggested form of
                guidance to the master on
                an approximate determination
                of ship's stability by means of
                the rolling period test   38

Appendix D   – Text of regulation 44 of the International
                Convention on Load Lines, 1966   41

Resolution A.715(17) – adopted on 6 November 1991   45

v

FOREWORD

The Code of Safe Practice for Ships Carrying Timber Deck Cargoes was first circulated by the Organization in 1972 and subsequently amended in 1978.

The continuing occurrence of casualties involving shift and loss of timber deck cargoes, the employment of larger and more sophisticated ships in this trade, the introduction of new techniques and the desirability of having more comprehensive safety recommendations in this particular maritime activity have made it necessary to revise and update the earlier document.

Although this Code is directed primarily at providing recommendations for the safe carriage of timber deck cargo, appendix B contains recommendations applicable to the under-deck stowage of logs.

CHAPTER 1 – GENERAL

1.1   Purpose

The purpose of this Code is to make recommendations on stowage, securing and other operational safety measures designed to ensure the safe transport of mainly timber deck cargoes.

1.2   Application

This Code applies to all ships of 24 m or more in length engaged in the carriage of timber deck cargoes. Ships that are provided with and making use of their timber load line should also comply with the requirements of the applicable regulation of the Load Line Convention (reproduced in appendix D).

1.3   Definitions

Except where expressly provided otherwise, the following definitions apply to the Code.

1.3.1 *Administration* means the Government of the State whose flag the ship is entitled to fly.

1.3.2 *Cant* means a log which is "slab-cut", i.e. ripped lengthwise so that the resulting thick pieces have two opposing, parallel flat sides and in some cases a third side which is sawn flat.

Note: The Code of Safe Practice for Ships Carrying Timber Deck Cargoes, 1991, comprises the annex to resolution A.715(17), the text of which is reproduced at the end of the present publication.

1

1.3.3 *Fall protection system* means a system which incorporates an adequate anchorage point, a safety harness worn by the person to be protected and a fall arrest device which, when attached to the anchorage point and harness, will permit normal personnel movement but lock immediately if any force is applied to the system.

1.3.4 *Organization* means the International Maritime Organization (IMO).

1.3.5 *Timber* means sawn wood or lumber, cants, logs, poles, pulpwood and all other type of timber in loose or packaged forms. The term does not include wood pulp or similar cargo.

1.3.6 *Timber deck cargo* means a cargo of timber carried on an uncovered part of a freeboard or superstructure deck. The term does not include wood pulp or similar cargo.

1.3.7 *Timber load line* means a special load line assigned to ships complying with certain conditions related to their construction set out in the International Convention on Load Lines and used when the cargo complies with the stowage and securing conditions of this Code.

1.3.8 *Weather deck* means the uppermost complete deck exposed to weather and sea.

CHAPTER 2 – STABILITY

2.1   The ship should be supplied with comprehensive stability information which takes into account timber deck cargo. Such information should enable the master, rapidly and simply, to obtain accurate guidance as to the stability of the ship under varying conditions of service. Comprehensive rolling period tables or diagrams have proved to be a very useful aid in verifying the actual stability conditions.

2.2   The stability of the ship at all times, including during the process of loading and unloading timber deck cargo, should be positive and to a standard acceptable to the Administration. It should be calculated having regard to:

    .1   the increased weight of the timber deck cargo due to:

    .1.1   absorption of water in dried or seasoned timber, and

    .1.2   ice accretion, if applicable;

    .2   variations in consumables;

    .3   the free surface effect of liquid in tanks; and

    .4   the weight of water trapped in broken spaces within the timber deck cargo and especially logs.

2.3 The master should:

    .1 cease all loading operations if a list develops for which there is no satisfactory explanation and it would be imprudent to continue loading;

    .2 before proceeding to sea, ensure that:

    .2.1 the ship is upright;

    .2.2 the ship has an adequate metacentric height; and

    .2.3 the ship meets the required stability criteria.

2.4 Ships carrying timber deck cargoes should operate, as far as possible, with a safe margin of stability and with a metacentric height which is consistent with safety requirements but such metacentric height should not be allowed to fall below the recommended minimum.*

2.5 However, excessive initial stability should be avoided as it will result in rapid and violent motion in heavy seas which will impose large sliding and racking forces on the cargo causing high stresses on the lashings. Operational experience indicates that metacentric height should preferably not exceed 3% of the breadth in order to prevent excessive accelerations in rolling provided that the relevant stability criteria are satisfied.* This recommendation may not apply to all ships and the master should take into consideration the stability information obtained from the ship's stability manual.

CHAPTER 3 – STOWAGE

3.1 General

3.1.1 Before timber deck cargo is loaded on any area of the weather deck:

    .1 hatch covers and other openings to spaces below that area should be securely closed and battened down;

    .2 air pipes and ventilators should be efficiently protected and check-valves or similar devices should be examined to ascertain their effectiveness against the entry of water;

    .3 accumulations of ice and snow on such area should be removed; and

    .4 it is normally preferable to have all deck lashings, uprights, etc., in position before loading on that specific area. This will be necessary should a preloading examination of securing equipment be required in the loading port.

3.1.2 The timber deck cargo should be so stowed that:

---

* Refer to the Recommendation on intact stability for passenger and cargo ships under 100 metres in length (resolution A.167(ES.IV)), as amended by resolution A.206(VII) with respect to ships carrying timber deck cargoes (reproduced in appendix C).

   .1   safe and satisfactory access to the crew's quarters, pilot boarding access, machinery spaces and all other areas regularly used in the necessary working of the ship is provided at all times;

   .2   where relevant, openings that give access to the areas described in 3.1.1.1 can be properly closed and secured against the entry of water;

   .3   safety equipment, devices for remote operation of valves and sounding pipes are left accessible; and

   .4   it is compact and will not interfere in any way with the navigation and necessary working of the ship.

3.1.3 During loading, the timber deck cargo should be kept free of any accumulations of ice and snow.

3.1.4 Upon completion of loading, and before sailing, a thorough inspection of the ship should be carried out. Soundings should also be taken to verify that no structural damage has occurred causing an ingress of water.

3.2   Height and extent of timber deck cargo

3.2.1 Subject to 3.2.2, the height of the timber deck cargo above the weather deck on a ship within a seasonal winter zone in winter should not exceed one third of the extreme breadth of the ship.

3.2.2 The height of the timber deck cargo should be restricted so that:

   .1   adequate visibility is assured;

   .2   a safe margin of stability is maintained at all stages of the voyage;

   .3   any forward-facing profile does not present overhanging shoulders to a head sea; and

   .4   the weight of the timber deck cargo does not exceed the designed maximum permissible load on the weather deck and hatches.

3.2.3 On ships provided with, and making use of, their timber load line, the timber deck cargo should be stowed so as to extend:

   .1   over the entire available length of the well or wells between superstructures and as close as practicable to end bulkheads;

   .2   at least to the after end of the aftermost hatchway in the case where there is no limiting superstructure at the after end;

   .3   athwartships as close as possible to the ship's sides, after making due allowance for obstructions such as guardrails, bulwark stays, uprights, pilot boarding access, etc., provided any area of broken stowage thus created at the side of the ship does not exceed a mean of 4% of the breadth; and

   .4   to at least the standard height of a superstructure other than a raised quarterdeck.

3.2.4 The basic principle for the safe carriage of any timber deck cargo is a solid stowage during all stages of the deck loading. This can only be achieved by constant supervision by shipboard personnel during the loading process.

3.2.5 Appendix A provides general advice on stowage practices which have proved to be effective for various types of timber deck cargoes.

CHAPTER 4 – SECURING

4.1 General

4.1.1 Every lashing should pass over the timber deck cargo and be shackled to eyeplates suitable and adequate for the intended purpose and efficiently attached to the deck stringer plate or other strengthened points. They should be installed in such a manner as to be, as far as practicable, in contact with the timber deck cargo throughout its full height.

4.1.2 All lashings and components used for securing should:
- .1 possess a breaking strength of not less than 133 kN;
- .2 after initial stressing, show an elongation of not more than 5% at 80% of their breaking strength; and
- .3 show no permanent deformation after having been subjected to a proof load of not less than 40% of their original breaking strength.

4.1.3 Every lashing should be provided with a tightening device or system so placed that it can safely and efficiently operate when required. The load to be produced by the tightening device or system should not be less than:
- .1 27 kN in the horizontal part; and
- .2 16 kN in the vertical part.

4.1.4 Upon completion and after the initial securing, the tightening device or system should be left with not less than half the threaded length of screw or of tightening capacity available for future use.

4.1.5 Every lashing should be provided with a device or an installation to permit the length of the lashing to be adjusted.

4.1.6 The spacing of the lashings should be such that the two lashings at each end of each length of continuous deck stow are positioned as close as practicable to the extreme end of the timber deck cargo.

4.1.7 If wire rope clips are used to make a joint in a wire lashing, the following conditions should be observed to avoid a significant reduction in strength:

.1 the number and size of rope clips utilized should be in proportion to the diameter of the wire rope and should not be less than four, each spaced at intervals of not less than 15 cm;

.2 the saddle portion of the clip should be applied to the live load segment and the U-bolt to the dead or shortened end segment;

.3 rope clips should be initially tightened so that they visibly penetrate into the wire rope and subsequently be re-tightened after the lashing has been stressed.

4.1.8 Greasing the threads of grips, clips, shackles and turnbuckles increases their holding capacity and prevents corrosion.

4.2 Uprights

4.2.1 Uprights should be fitted when required by the nature, height or character of the timber deck cargo.

4.2.2 When uprights are fitted, they should:
.1 be made of steel or other suitable material of adequate strength, taking into account the breadth of the deck cargo;

.2 be spaced at intervals not exceeding 3 m;

.3 be fixed to the deck by angles, metal sockets or equally efficient means; and

.4 if deemed necessary, be further secured by a metal bracket to a strengthened point, i.e. bulwark, hatch coaming.

4.3 Loose or packaged sawn timber

4.3.1 The timber deck cargo should be secured throughout its length by independent lashings.

4.3.2 Subject to 4.3.3, the maximum spacing of the lashings referred to above should be determined by the maximum height of the timber deck cargo in the vicinity of the lashings:
.1 for a height of 4 m and below, the spacing should be 3 m;

.2 for heights of above 4 m, the spacing should be 1.5 m.

4.3.3 The packages stowed at the upper outboard edge of the stow should be secured by at least two lashings each.

4.3.4 When the outboard stow of the timber deck cargo is in lengths of less than 3.6 m, the spacing of the lashings should be reduced as necessary or other suitable provisions made to suit the length of timber.

4.3.5 Rounded angle pieces of suitable material and design should be used along the upper outboard edge of the stow to bear the stress and permit free reeving of the lashings.

4.4 Logs, poles, cants or similar cargo

4.4.1 The timber deck cargo should be secured throughout its length by independent lashings spaced not more than 3 m apart.

4.4.2 If the timber deck cargo is stowed over the hatches and higher, it should, in addition to being secured by the lashings recommended in 4.4.1, be further secured by:

.1 a system of athwartship lashings (hog lashings) joining each port and starboard pair of uprights near the top of the stow and at other appropriate levels as appropriate for the height of the stow; and

.2 a lashing system to tighten the stow whereby a dual continuous wire rope (wiggle wire) is passed from side to side over the cargo and held continuously through a series of snatch blocks or other suitable device, held in place by foot wires.

4.4.3 The dual continuous wire rope, referred to in 4.4.2.2, should be led to a winch or other tensioning device to facilitate further tightening.

4.4.4 The recommendation of 4.3.5 should apply to a timber deck cargo of cants.

4.5 Testing, examination and certification

4.5.1 All lashing and components used for the securing of the timber deck cargo should be tested, marked and certified according to national regulations or an appropriate standard of an internationally recognized standards institute. Copies of the appropriate certificate should be kept on board.

4.5.2 No treatments which could hide defects or reduce mechanical properties or strength should be applied after testing.

4.5.3 A visual examination of lashings and components should be made at intervals not exceeding 12 months.

4.5.4 A visual examination of all securing points on the ship, including those on the uprights, if fitted, should be performed before loading the timber deck cargo. Any damage should be satisfactorily repaired.

4.6 Lashing plans

One or more lashing plans complying with the recommendations of this Code should be provided and maintained on board a ship carrying timber deck cargo.

CHAPTER 5 - PERSONNEL PROTECTION AND SAFETY DEVICES

5.1   Suitable protective clothing and equipment, such as studded boots or studded overshoes and hard hats, should be provided for the protection of crew members and workers involved in loading, securing or discharging operations.

5.2   During the course of the voyage, if there is no convenient passage for the crew on or below the deck of the ship giving safe means of access from the accommodation to all parts used in the necessary working of the ship, guard lines or rails, not more than 330 mm apart vertically, should be provided on each side of the deck cargo to a height of at least 1 m above the cargo. In addition, a lifeline, preferably wire rope, set up taut with a tightening device should be provided as near as practicable to the centreline of the ship. The stanchion supports to all guardrails or lifelines should be spaced so as to prevent undue sagging. Where the cargo is uneven, a safe walking surface of not less than 600 mm in width should be fitted over the cargo and effectively secured beneath, or adjacent to, the lifeline.

5.3   Fencing or means of closing should be provided for all openings in the stow such as at masthouses, winches, etc.

5.4   Where uprights are not fitted or where alternatives to the provisions of 5.2 are permitted, a walkway of substantial construction should be provided having an even walking surface and consisting of two fore and aft sets of guardlines or rails about 1 m apart, each having a minimum of three courses of guardlines or rails to a height of not less than 1 m above the walking surface. Such guardlines or rails should be supported by rigid stanchions spaced not more than 3 m apart and lines should be set up taut by tightening devices.

5.5   As an alternative to 5.2, 5.3 and 5.4, a lifeline, preferably wire rope, may be erected above the timber deck cargo such that a crew member equipped with a fall protection system can hook on to it and work about the timber deck cargo. The lifeline should be:

.1   erected about 2 m above the timber deck cargo as near as practicable to the centreline of the ship;

.2   stretched sufficiently taut with a tightening device to support a fallen crew member without collapse or failure.

5.6   Properly constructed ladders, steps or ramps fitted with guard lines or handrails should be provided from the top of the cargo to the deck, and in other cases where the cargo is stepped, in order to provide reasonable access.

5.7   Personnel safety equipment referred to in this chapter should be kept in an easily accessible place.

CHAPTER 6 – ACTION TO BE TAKEN DURING THE VOYAGE

6.1 Tightening of lashings

6.1.1 It is of paramount importance that all lashings be carefully examined and tightened at the beginning of the voyage as the vibration and working of the ship will cause the cargo to settle and compact. They should be further examined at regular intervals during the voyage and tightened as necessary.

6.1.2 Entries of all examinations and adjustments to lashings should be made in the ship's log-book.

6.2 Voyage planning and ship handling

6.2.1 The master should plan the voyage so as to avoid potential severe weather and sea conditions. To this effect, weather reports, weather facsimiles or weather routeing agencies should be consulted.

6.2.2 In cases where severe weather and sea conditions are unavoidable, masters should be conscious of the need to reduce speed and/or alter course at an early stage in order to minimize the forces imposed on the cargo, structure and lashings. The lashings are not designed to provide a means of securing against imprudent ship handling in heavy weather. There can be no substitute for good seamanship.

6.3 Listing during voyage

If a list occurs that is not caused by normal use of consumables (water and fuel), such a list can probably be attributed to one of three causes, or possibly a combination of same.

Cargo shift

6.3.1 A major shift of deck cargo will obviously be immediately apparent. Deck cargo may however have shifted imperceptibly or there may have been a shift of cargo below decks. An immediate examination should determine whether or not cargo has shifted and if this is the case the master will have several remedies available to him depending upon the exact circumstances.

6.3.2 The ballasting and transferring of ballast or fuel to reduce or correct a list caused by a shifted cargo should, however, be carefully considered since this action would, in all probability, result in a far greater list if the cargo should subsequently shift to the other side.

6.3.3 As any cargo shift will in most cases occur in adverse weather conditions, sending crew to release or tighten the lashings on a moving or shifted cargo may well represent a greater hazard than retaining an overhanging load. A moving or shifted timber deck cargo should only be jettisoned after careful consideration; jettisoning is unlikely to improve the situation as the whole cargo stack would probably not fall at once. Severe damage may also be sustained by the propeller if it is still turning when timber is jettisoned.

Water ingress

6.3.4 The possibility of water ingress should immediately be determined by sounding throughout the ship. In the event that unexplained water is detected, all available pumps should be used to bring the situation under control. Subsequent actions will obviously depend upon whether or not such ingress of water can be controlled by use of pumps.

Angle of loll

6.3.5 If the rolling of the ship prior to the detection of the list has been exceptionally slow and the ship has returned to the upright position in a sluggish manner, this will indicate that the ship has little or no meta-centric height remaining. The list is therefore due to the ship lolling to one side and having no righting arm to return it to the upright position. This situation may be rectified by either adding weight to the low part of the ship (ballasting double bottom tanks) or removing weight from the high part (deck cargo). Of the two options, ballasting is usually preferable and if empty divided double bottom space is available, the tank on the lower side should be ballasted first in order to immediately provide additional metacentric height – after which the tank on the high side should also be ballasted. However, special care should be taken in ballasting and deballasting to rectify the situation since this may cause a far greater list to the other side.

6.4   Notification

If a whole or partial timber deck load is either jettisoned or accidentally lost overboard the attention of the master is drawn to chapter V of the International Convention for the Safety of Life at Sea which, *inter alia*, requires a master to communicate information on a direct danger to navigation by all means at his disposal, to ships in the vicinity, and also to the competent authorities at the first point on the coast with which he can communicate. It is required that such information should include the kind of danger (in this case a timber deck load), the position of the danger when last observed, and the time and date (co-ordinated universal time) when the danger was last observed.

Appendix A

Advice on stowage practices

1   GENERAL

1.1   The stowage practices described in this appendix have been found to achieve satisfactory results, provided that account is taken of the recommendations of chapters 1 to 6. Although specific conditions may dictate a departure from these guidelines, the basic principle as detailed in 1.2 should nevertheless be adhered to.

1.2   The basic principle for the safe carriage of timber deck cargo is, as indicated earlier, to make the stow as solid and compact as practicable. The purpose of this is to:

   .1   prevent slack in the stow which could cause the lashings to slacken;

   .2   produce a binding effect within the stow; and

   .3   reduce to a minimum the permeability of the stow.

1.3   Lashings prevent deck cargo from shifting by increasing the friction due to pre-stress forces and counteracting forces on the stow in the direction of possible shifting. The lashings should meet the following criteria:

   .1   the strength of all lashing elements should be at least equal to that recommended in the Code; and

   .2   the necessary tension should be maintained during the whole voyage.

1.4   The shifting of timber deck cargo is due mainly to the following causes which may occur singly or together:

   .1   lashings becoming slack due to compaction of the cargo during the voyage, unsuitable devices for tightening the lashing systems and/or inadequate strength of the lashings;

   .2   movement of the cargo across the hatch covers due to insufficient friction, particularly in ice and snow;

   .3   inadequate strength of the uprights due to poor material properties and/or excessive forces;

   .4   heavy rolling or pitching of the ship;

   .5   impact from heavy seas.

1.5   Great care should be taken to keep the ship in an upright condition during loading as even a slight list will impose a considerable load on the retaining uprights. The necessity for prudent ship handling during the voyage cannot be overstressed; imprudent ship handling can nullify even the best of stowages.

1.6 The lashings should be in accordance with chapter 4 of the Code and may comprise the following types:

.1 Hog lashings are normally used over the second and third tiers and may be set "hand tight" between stanchions. The weight of the upper tiers when loaded on top of these wires will further tighten them (see figure 1).

.2 Wire rope lashings which are used in addition to chain lashings. Each of these may pass over the stow from side to side and loop completely around the uppermost tier. Turnbuckles are fitted in each lashing to provide means for tightening the lashing at sea (see figure 2).

.3 Wiggle wires which are fitted in the manner of a shoelace to tighten the stow. These wires are passed over the stow and continuously through a series of snatch blocks, held in place by foot wires. Turnbuckles are fitted from the top of the footwire into the wiggle wire in order to keep the lashings tight at sea (see figures 3 and 4).

.4 Chain lashings which are passed over the top of the stow and secured to substantial padeyes or other securing points at the outboard extremities of the cargo. Turnbuckles are fitted in each lashing to provide means for tightening the lashing at sea (see figure 5).

1.7 Systems for securing timber deck cargoes are shown in figures 3, 4, 5, 6 and 7.

2   PACKAGED TIMBER AND CANTS

2.1 Timber packages are usually bundled by bandings fastened mechanically (hard bundled) or by hand (soft bundled). The packages may not have standard dimensions and they are not always flush at both ends. The stowage problem is compounded by differences in the lengths of packaged timber when the packages are stowed on board the ship. Moreover, the master of the ship often has no influence on the order in which the packages are delivered.

2.2 Packages which contain random lengths likely to disrupt the compaction of the stow should not be loaded on deck. Other packages of random lengths capable of compact stowage may be loaded on deck in a fore-and-aft direction but not on exposed surfaces or in the stowage outboard of the hatch coamings (see figures 8 and 9).

2.3 Packages for deck stowage should be solidly made up. They should have bands adequate to prevent slackening or disintegration of the package during the voyage, which could cause a loosening of the stow as a whole. Slack bands on the top surface of the deck cargo are dangerous foot traps.

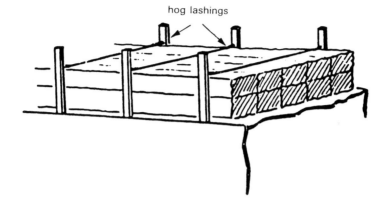

Figure 1

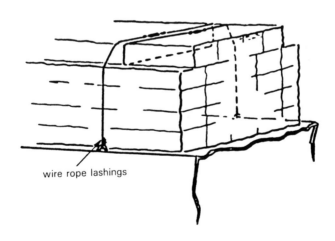

Figure 2

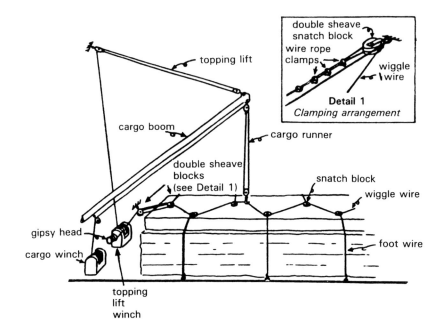

Figure 3

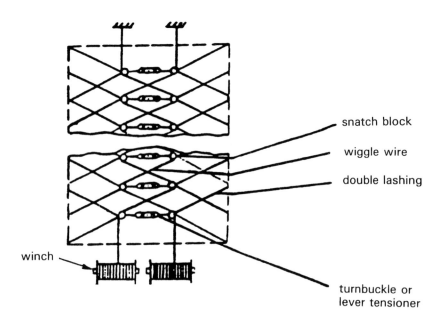

Figure 4

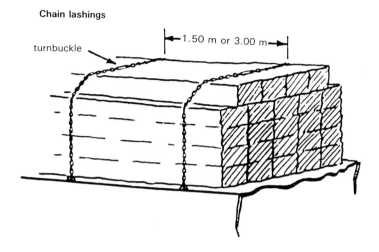

Chain lashings

turnbuckle

1.50 m or 3.00 m

Figure 5

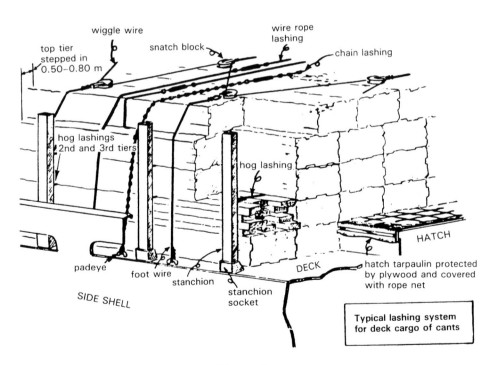

wiggle wire

wire rope lashing

top tier stepped in 0.50–0.80 m

snatch block

chain lashing

hog lashings 2nd and 3rd tiers

hog lashing

HATCH

padeye

foot wire

stanchion

stanchion socket

DECK

hatch tarpaulin protected by plywood and covered with rope net

SIDE SHELL

Typical lashing system for deck cargo of cants

Figure 6

15

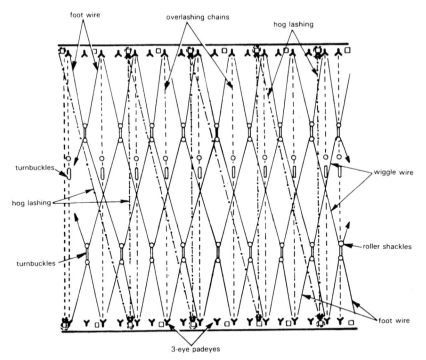

Note: Roller shackles to be affixed between all foot wires and wiggle wires and at least two turnbuckles to be inserted between the wiggle wire and the footwire on each side (port and starboard).

Figure 7

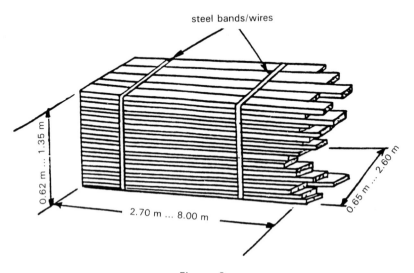

Figure 8

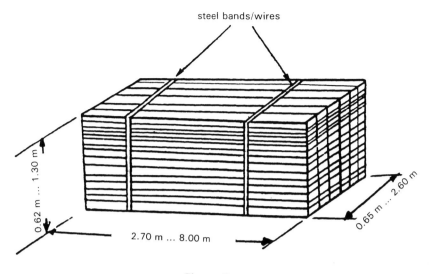

steel bands/wires

0.62 m ... 1.30 m

2.70 m ... 8.00 m

0.65 m ... 2.60 m

Figure 9

2.4 Cants are usually bundled by banding, but the irregularities caused by varying thicknesses and curved sides make compact bundling very difficult to achieve. Because of these factors, considerable broken stowage is encountered as well. The tendency is for the packages to assume a rounded cross-section within the bands due to the curved sides of the individual pieces (see figure 10).

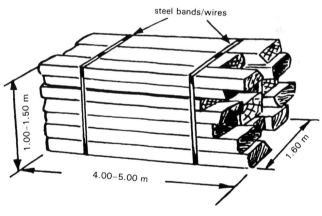

steel bands/wires

1.00–1.50 m

4.00–5.00 m

1.60 m

Figure 10

2.5 A solid stow of packaged timber is not always possible as the packages of timber have different measurements, may be partially soft bundles, and gaps may exist between the packages. It is essential, however, that the upper tier and outboard packages be stowed as compactly as possible and the upper tiers chocked as necessary.

2.6   The methods used to stow cargoes of loose timber for transport cannot always be applied to the transport of packaged timber as:

   .1   packaged timber cannot be stowed to give a compactness as tight as that achieved with loose timber, and lashings may therefore be less effective;

   .2   packaged timber cannot be stowed between the uprights as densely and with so few gaps as loose timber. The uprights may consequently have to sustain greater loads when packaged timber is being carried and may absorb the forces generated by the cargo when it is moving.

2.7   Before commencing to load on the deck or hatches, a firm and level stowage surface should be prepared. Dunnage, where used, should be of rough lumber and should be placed in the direction which will spread the load across the ship's underdeck structure and assist in draining.

2.8   Due to the system of athwartship lashing, the stowage of packages should generally be in the fore-and-aft direction; the wings of the upper two tiers should always be in the fore-and-aft direction. It is advisable to have one or more non-adjacent tiers stowed athwartships when above the level of the hatches in order to produce a binding effect within the cargo. Also, athwartship packages should be carried above the hatches to interlock the load. If packages with great differences in length are to be loaded, the longest packages should be stowed fore and aft outboard. Short packages should be confined to the inner portions of the stowage. Only packages flush at both ends can be stowed athwartships (see figures 11, 12 and 13).

dunnage

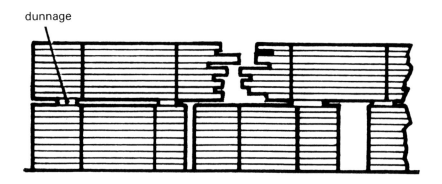

Figure 11

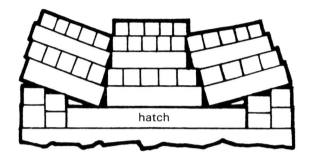

Figure 12

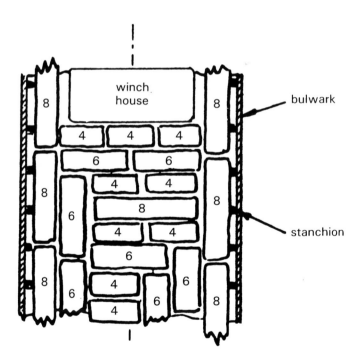

Figure 13

2.9 The timber should be loaded to produce a compact stow with a surface as level as practicable. Throughout the loading, a level and firm stowage surface should be prepared on each working tier. Rough dunnage, if used, should be spread over at least three adjacent packages to produce a binding effect within the stow, particularly in the wings.

2.10 Any gaps occurring around packages in which the cargo may work at sea, such as in the vicinity of hatch coamings and deck obstructions, should be filled with loose timber, efficiently chocked off or effectively bridged over. For this purpose a supply of timber chocking material should be made available to the ship.

2.11 Packages at the outboard edges of the stow should be positioned so that they do not extend over the padeyes and obstruct the vertical load of the athwartship lashings. The end of each deck stow should be flush in order to minimize overhangs to resist the influence of green seas and to avoid the ingress of water.

2.12 Large heavy boards and squares of timber, when loaded on deck in combination with packages, should preferably be stowed separately. When placed in upper tiers, heavy pieces of timber tend to work loose at sea and cause some breaking of packages. In the event that boards and squares are stowed on top of packages they should be efficiently restrained from movement.

2.13 When the final tier is loaded on a large number of tiers, it may be stepped in from the outer edge of the stow about 0.5–0.8 m (a half package).

3   LOGS

3.1 If logs are loaded on deck together with packaged timber, the two types of timber should not be intermixed.

3.2 Logs should generally be stowed in a fore-and-aft direction to give a slightly crowned top surface such that each log is adequately restrained from movement when the system of securing is in place and set up taut.

3.3 In order to achieve a compact stow, the butt of each log or sling of logs should not be in the same athwartship plane as those adjacent to it.

3.4 In order to achieve a more secure stowage of logs when stowed on deck, a continuous wire (hog wire) should be utilized at each hatch meeting the specifications of chapter 4 of this Code. Such hog wire should be installed in the following manner:

> .1 At approximately three quarters of the height of the uprights, the hog wire should be rove through a padeye attached to the uprights at this level so as to run transversely, connecting the

respective port and starboard uprights. The hog lashing wire should not be too tight when laid so that it becomes taut when overstowed with other logs.

.2   A second hog wire may be applied in a similar manner if the height of the hatch cover is less than 2 m. Such second hog wire should be installed approximately 1 m above the hatch covers.

.3   The aim of having the hog wires applied in this manner is to assist in obtaining as even a tension as possible throughout, thus producing an inboard pull on the respective uprights.

4   PULP WOOD AND PIT-PROPS

4.1   When these items are stowed in the manner described below, good compaction of the deck cargo can be obtained.

.1   In the deck area clear of the line of hatches, the cargo should be stowed in the athwartship direction, canted inboard by some cargo laid fore and aft in the scuppers.

.2   At the centre of the stow, along the line of hatches, the cargo should be laid in the fore-and-aft direction when the wing cargo has reached hatch height.

.3   At the completion of loading, the cargo should have a level surface with a slight crown towards the centre.

4.2   To prevent the cargo from being washed out from below its lashings, it is recommended that nets or tarpaulins be used as follows:

.1   the ends of each continuous section of deck cargo, if not stowed flush with the superstructure bulkhead, may be fitted with a net or tarpaulin stretched and secured over the athwartship vertical surface;

.2   over the forward end of each continuous section of deck cargo and in the waist of the ship the top surface may be fitted with a net or tarpaulin stretched and secured across the breadth of the cargo and brought down the outboard vertical sides to securing points at deck level.

Appendix B

General guidelines for the under-deck stowage of logs

1   The purpose of this appendix is to recommend safe practices for the under-deck stowage of logs and other operational safety measures designed to ensure the safe transport of such cargoes.

2   Prior to loading:

    .1 each cargo space configuration (length, breadth and depth), the cubic bale capacity of the respective cargo spaces, the various lengths of logs to be loaded, the cubic volume (log average), and the capacity of the gear to be used to load the logs should be determined;

    .2 using the above information, a pre-stow plan should be developed to allow the maximum utilization of the available space; the better the under-deck stowage, the more cargo can safely be carried on deck;

    .3 the cargo spaces and related equipment should be examined to determine whether the condition of structural members, framework and equipment could affect the safe carriage of the log cargo. Any damage discovered during such an examination should be repaired in an appropriate manner;

    .4 the bilge suction screens should be examined to ensure they are clean, effective and properly maintained to prevent the admission of debris into the bilge piping system;

    .5 the bilge wells should be free of extraneous material such as wood bark and wood splinters;

    .6 the capacity of the bilge pumping system should be ascertained. A properly maintained and operating system is crucial for the safety of the ship. A portable dewatering pump of sufficient capacity and lift will provide additional insurance against a clogged bilge line;

    .7 side sparring, pipe guards, etc., designed to protect internal hull members should be in place; and

    .8 the master should ensure that the opening and closing of any high ballast tank dump valves are properly logged. Given that such high ballast tanks are necessary to facilitate loading and bearing in mind regulation 22(1) of the International Convention on Load Lines, 1966, which requires a screw-down valve fitted in gravity overboard drain lines, the master should ensure that the dump valves are properly monitored to preclude the accidental readmission of water into these tanks. Leaving these tanks open to the sea could lead to an apparently inexplicable list, a shift of deck cargo, and potential capsize.

3   During loading operations:

.1   each lift of logs should be hoisted aboard the ship in close proximity to the ship to minimize any potential swinging of the lift;

.2   the possibility of damage to the ship and the safety of those who work in the cargo spaces should be considered. The logs should not be swinging when lowered into the space. The hatch coaming should be used, as necessary, to eliminate any swinging of the logs by gently resting the load against the inside of the coaming, or on it, prior to lowering;

.3   the logs should be stowed compactly, thereby eliminating as many voids as is practicable. The amount and the vertical centre of gravity of the logs stowed under deck will govern the amount of cargo that can be safely stowed on deck. In considering this principle, the heaviest logs should be loaded first into the cargo spaces;

.4   logs should generally be stowed compactly in a fore-and-aft direction, with the longer lengths towards the forward and after areas of the space. If there is a void in the space between the fore and aft lengths, it should be filled with logs stowed athwartships so as to fill in the void across the breadth of the spaces as completely as the length of the logs permits;

.5   where the logs in the spaces can only be stowed fore and aft in one length, any remaining void forward or after should be filled with logs stowed athwartships so as to fill in the void across the breadth of the space as completely as the length of the logs permits;

.6   athwartship voids should be filled tier by tier as loading progresses;

.7   butt ends of the logs should be alternately reversed to achieve a more level stowage, except where excess sheer on the inner bottom is encountered;

.8   extreme pyramiding of logs should be avoided to the greatest extent possible. If the breadth of the space is greater than the breadth of the hatch opening, pyramiding may be avoided by sliding fore and aft loaded logs into the ends of the port and starboard sides of the space. This sliding of logs into the ends of the port and starboard sides of the space should commence early in the loading process (after reaching a height of approximately 2 m above the inner bottom) and should continue throughout the loading process;

.9 it may be necessary to use loose tackle to manoeuvre heavy logs into the under-deck areas clear of the hatchways. Blocks, purchases and other loose tackle should be attached to suitably reinforced fixtures such as eyebolts or padeyes provided for this purpose. However, if this procedure is followed, care should be taken to avoid overloading the gear;

.10 a careful watch by ship's personnel should be maintained throughout the loading to ensure that no structural damage occurs. Any damage which affects the seaworthiness of the ship should be repaired;

.11 when the logs are stowed to a height of about 1 m below the forward or after athwartship hatch coaming, the size of the lift of logs should be reduced to facilitate stowing of the remaining area; and

.12 logs in the hatch coaming area should be stowed as compactly as possible to maximum capacity.

4   After loading, the ship should be thoroughly examined to ascertain its structural condition. Bilges should be sounded to verify the ship's watertight integrity.

5   During the voyage:

.1 the ship's heeling angle and rolling period should be checked, in a seaway, on a regular basis;

.2 wedges, wastes, hammers and portable pump, if provided, should be stored in an easily accessible place; and

.3 the master or a responsible officer should ensure that it is safe to enter an enclosed cargo space by:

.3.1 ensuring that the space has been thoroughly ventilated by natural or mechanical means;

.3.2 testing the atmosphere of the space at different levels for oxygen deficiency and harmful vapour where suitable instruments are available; and

.3.3 requiring self-contained breathing apparatus to be worn by all persons entering the space where there is any doubt as to the adequacy of ventilation or testing before entry.

Appendix C

Recommendation on intact stability for passenger and cargo ships under 100 metres in length, as amended with respect to ships carrying deck cargoes*

1   SCOPE

1.1   The provisions given hereunder are recommended for new decked seagoing passenger and cargo ships (other than fishing vessels) under 100 m in length.

1.2   Administrations are invited to adopt, for all conditions of loading, the stability criteria given in 5 below unless they are satisfied that operating experience justifies departures therefrom.

2   GENERAL PRECAUTIONS AGAINST CAPSIZING

2.1   Compliance with the stability criteria does not ensure immunity against capsizing regardless of the circumstances or absolve the master from his responsibilities. Masters should therefore exercise prudence and good seamanship having regard to the season of the year, weather forecasts and the navigational zone and should take the appropriate action as to speed and course warranted by the prevailing circumstances.

2.2   Care should be taken that the cargo allocated to the ship is capable of being stowed so that compliance with the criteria can be achieved. If necessary, the amount should be limited to the extent that ballast weight may be required.

2.3   Before a voyage commences care should be taken to ensure that the cargo and sizeable pieces of equipment have been properly stowed or lashed so as to minimize the possibility of both longitudinal and lateral shifting while at sea, under the effect of acceleration caused by rolling and pitching.

3   CALCULATION OF STABILITY CURVES

The methods and procedures employed for calculating stability righting arms should be in accordance with appendix 1, and the degree of accuracy obtained should be acceptable to the Administration.

---

* The text of the Recommendation on intact stability for passenger and cargo ships under 100 metres in length was adopted by resolution A.167(ES.IV) and amended by resolution A.206(VII) with respect to ships carrying timber deck cargoes. The Recommendation, as amended, is reproduced here with minor editorial changes.

4   ASSESSMENT OF COMPLIANCE WITH CRITERIA

4.1   For the purpose of assessing in general whether the criteria are met, stability curves should be drawn for the main loading conditions intended by the owner in respect of the ship's operations.

4.2   If the owner does not supply sufficiently detailed information regarding such loading conditions, calculations should be made for the standard conditions given in appendix 2.

4.3   In all cases calculations should be based on the assumptions shown in appendix 2.

5   RECOMMENDED CRITERIA

5.1   The following criteria are recommended for passenger and cargo ships:

   .1   The area under the righting lever curve (GZ curve) should not be less than 0.055 metre radians up to $\theta = 30°$ angle of heel and not less than 0.09 metre radians up to $\theta = 40°$ or the angle of flooding θ_f,* if this angle is less than 40°.

   Additionally, the area under the righting lever curve (GZ curve) between the angles of heel of 30° and 40° or between 30° and θ_f, if this angle is less than 40°, should not be less than 0.03 metre radians.

   .2   The righting lever GZ should be at least 0.20 m at an angle of heel equal to or greater than 30°.

   .3   The maximum righting arm should occur at an angle of heel preferably exceeding 30° but not less than 25°.

   .4   The initial metacentric height GM_0 should not be less than 0.15 m.

5.2   For ships loaded with timber deck cargoes and provided that the cargo extends longitudinally between superstructures** transversely for the full beam of the ship after due allowance for a rounded gunwale not exceeding 4% of the breadth of the ship and/or securing the supporting uprights and which remains securely fixed at large angle of heel, an Administration may apply the following criteria in substitution for criteria given in 5.1 above:

---

* θ_f is an angle of heel at which openings in the hull, superstructures or deckhouses which cannot be closed weathertight immerse. In applying this criterion, small openings through which progressive flooding cannot take place need not be considered as open.
** Where there is no limiting superstructure at the after end, the timber deck cargo shall extend at least to the after end of the aftermost hatchway.

    .1   The area under the righting lever (GZ curve) should not be less than 0.08 metre radians up to $\theta = 40°$ or the angle of flooding if this angle is less than 40°.

    .2   The maximum value of the righting lever (GZ) should be at least 0.25 m.

    .3   At all times during a voyage the metacentric height GM_0 should be positive after correction for the free surface effects of liquid in tanks and, where appropriate, the absorption of water by the deck cargo and/or ice accretion on the exposed surfaces. Additionally, in the departure condition the metacentric height should be not less than 0.10 m.

5.3   The following additional criteria are recommended for passenger ships:

    .1   The angle of heel on account of crowding of passengers to one side as defined in appendix 2, 2.11, should not exceed 10°.

    .2   The angle of heel on account of turning should not exceed 10° when calculated using the following formula:

$$M_R = 0.02 \frac{V_0^2}{L} \Delta(KG - \frac{d}{2})$$

where:

M_R = heeling moment in metre-tons

V_0 = service speed in metres per second

L = length of ship at waterline in metres

Δ = displacement in metric tons

d = mean draught in metres

KG = height of centre of gravity above keel in metres

5.4   The criteria mentioned in 5.1, 5.2 and 5.3 above fix minimum values, but no maximum values are recommended. It is advisable to avoid excessive values, since these might lead to acceleration forces which could be prejudicial to the ship, its complement, its equipment and to the safe carriage of the cargo.

5.5   Where antirolling devices are installed in a ship, the Administration should be satisfied that the above criteria can be maintained when the devices are in operation.

5.6   A number of influences such as beam wind on ships with large windage area, icing of topsides, water trapped on deck, rolling characteristics, following seas, etc., adversely affect stability and the Administration is advised to take these into account so far as is deemed necessary.

5.7   Regard should be paid to the possible adverse effects on stability where certain bulk cargoes are carried. In this connection, attention should be paid to the Code of Safe Practice for Solid Bulk Cargoes. Ships carrying grain in bulk should comply with the criteria mentioned in 5.1 above, in addition to the stability requirements in chapter VI of the International Convention for the Safety of Life at Sea, 1960.

6   INCLINING TEST

6.1   When construction is finished, each ship should undergo an inclining test, actual displacement and co-ordinates of the centre of gravity being determined for the light ship condition.

6.2   The Administration may allow the inclining test of an individual ship to be dispensed with, provided basic stability data are available from the inclining test of a sister ship.

7   STABILITY INFORMATION

7.1   The master of any ship to which the present Recommendation applies should receive information which will enable him to assess with ease and certainty the stability of his ship in different service conditions. A duplicate of this information should be communicated to the Administration.

7.2   Stability information should comprise:

.1   stability characteristics of typical loading conditions;

.2   information in the form of tables or diagrams which will enable the master to assess the stability of his ship and verify whether it is sufficient in all loading conditions differing from the standard ones. This information should include, in particular, a curve or table giving, as a function of the draughts, the required initial metacentric height GM_0 (or any other stability parameter) which ensures that the stability is in compliance with the criteria given in 5.1 above;

.3   information on the proper use of antirolling devices if these are installed in the ship;

.4   additionally, information enabling the ship's master to determine the initial metacentric height GM_0 by means of rolling test, as described in the annex to the memorandum to Administrations reproduced in appendix 3, would be desirable;

.5   notes on the corrections to be made to the initial metacentric height GM_0 to take account of free surface liquids;

.6   for ships carrying timber deck cargoes, the Administration may deem it necessary that the master be given information setting out the changes in deck cargo from that shown in the loading conditions, when the permeability of the deck cargo is significantly different from 25%;

.7   for ships carrying timber deck cargoes, conditions should be shown indicating the maximum permissible amount of deck cargo having regard to the lightest stowage rate likely to be met in service.

Appendix 1
Calculation of stability curves

1   GENERAL

1.1   Hydrostatic and stability curves should normally be prepared on a designed trim basis. However, where the operating trim or the form and arrangement of the ship are such that change in trim has an appreciable effect on righting arms, such change in trim should be taken into account.

1.2   The calculations should take into account the volume to the upper surface of the deck sheathing. In the case of wood ships, the dimensions should be taken to the outside of the hull planking.

2   SUPERSTRUCTURES, DECKHOUSES, ETC., WHICH MAY BE TAKEN INTO ACCOUNT

2.1   Enclosed superstructures complying with regulation 3(10)(b) of the 1966 Load Line Convention may be taken into account.

2.2   The second tier of similarly enclosed superstructures may also be taken into account.

2.3   Deckhouses on the freeboard deck may be taken into account, provided that they comply with the conditions for enclosed superstructures laid down in regulation 3(10)(b) of the 1966 Load Line Convention.

2.4   Where deckhouses comply with the above conditions, except that no additional exit is provided to a deck above, such deckhouses should not be taken into account; however, any deck openings inside such deckhouses shall be considered as closed even where no means of closure are provided.

2.5   Deckhouses, the doors of which do not comply with the requirements of regulation 12 of the 1966 Load Line Convention should not be taken into account; however, any deck openings inside the deckhouse are regarded as closed where their means of closure comply with the requirements of regulations 15, 17 or 18 of the 1966 Load Line Convention.

2.6   Deckhouses on decks above the freeboard deck should not be taken into account, but openings within them may be regarded as closed.

2.7   Superstructures and deckhouses not regarded as enclosed can, however, be taken into account in stability calculations up to the angle at which their openings are flooded. (At this angle, the statical stability curve should show one or more steps, and in subsequent computations the flooded space should be considered non-existent.)

2.8   In cases where the ship would sink due to flooding through any openings, the stability curve should be cut short at the corresponding angle of flooding and the ship should be considered to have entirely lost its stability.

2.9   Small openings such as those for passing wires or chains, tackle and anchors, and also holes of scuppers, discharge and sanitary pipes should not be considered as open if they submerge at an angle of inclination more than 30°. If they submerge at an angle of 30° or less, these openings should be assumed open if the Administration considers this to be a source of significant flooding.

2.10   Trunks may be taken into account. Hatchways may also be taken into account having regard to the effectiveness of their closures.

3   EFFECT OF LIQUID IN TANKS

3.1   For all conditions, the initial metacentric height and the stability curves should be corrected for the effect of free surfaces of liquids in tanks in accordance with the following assumptions:

> .1   Tanks which are taken into consideration when determining the effect of liquids on stability at all angles of inclination should include single tanks or combinations of tanks for each kind of liquid (including those for water ballast) which according to the service conditions can simultaneously have free surfaces.

> .2   For the purpose of determining this free surface correction, the tanks assumed slack should be those which develop the greatest free surface moment, $M_{f.s.}$ at a 30° inclination, when in the 50% full condition.

> .3   The value of $M_{f.s.}$ for each tank may be derived from the formula:

$$M_{f.s.} = vb\gamma k\sqrt{\delta}$$

where:

$M_{f.s.}$ = the free surface moment at any inclination in metre-tons

v = the tank total capacity in cubic metres

b = the tank maximum breadth in metres

γ = the specific weight of liquid in the tank in metric tons per cubic metre

δ = $\dfrac{v}{blh}$ = the tank block coefficient

h = the tank maximum height in metres

l = the tank maximum length in metres

k = dimensionless coefficient to be determined from the following table according to the ratio b/h. The intermediate values are determined by interpolation (linear or graphic).

.4 Small tanks, which satisfy the following condition using the value of k corresponding to the angle of inclination of 30°, need not be included in computation:

$$\frac{vb\gamma k\sqrt{\delta}}{\Delta_{min}} < 0.01 \text{ m}$$

where:

Δ_{min} = minimum ship displacement in metric tons.

.5 The usual remainder of liquids in the empty tanks is not taken into account in computation.

Table of values for coefficient k
for calculating free surface corrections

$$k = \frac{\sin\theta}{12}\left(1 + \frac{\tan^2\theta}{2}\right) \times b/h \qquad\qquad k = \frac{\cos\theta}{8}\left(1 + \frac{\tan\theta}{b/h}\right) - \frac{\cos\theta}{12(b/h)^2}\left(1 + \frac{\cot^2\theta}{2}\right)$$

where $\cot\theta \geqslant b/h$ where $\cot\theta \leqslant b/h$

θ / b/h	5°	10°	15°	20°	30°	40°	45°	50°	60°	70°	75°	80°	90°	θ / b/h
20	0.11	0.12	0.12	0.12	0.11	0.10	0.09	0.09	0.07	0.05	0.04	0.03	0.01	20
10	0.07	0.11	0.12	0.12	0.11	0.10	0.10	0.09	0.07	0.05	0.04	0.03	0.01	10
5	0.04	0.07	0.10	0.11	0.11	0.11	0.10	0.10	0.08	0.07	0.06	0.05	0.03	5
3	0.02	0.04	0.07	0.09	0.11	0.11	0.11	0.10	0.09	0.08	0.07	0.06	0.04	3
2	0.01	0.03	0.04	0.06	0.09	0.11	0.11	0.11	0.10	0.09	0.09	0.08	0.06	2
1.5	0.01	0.02	0.03	0.05	0.07	0.10	0.11	0.11	0.11	0.11	0.10	0.10	0.08	1.5
1	0.01	0.01	0.02	0.03	0.05	0.07	0.09	0.10	0.12	0.13	0.13	0.13	0.13	1
0.75	0.01	0.01	0.02	0.02	0.04	0.05	0.07	0.08	0.12	0.15	0.16	0.16	0.17	0.75
0.5	0.00	0.01	0.01	0.02	0.02	0.04	0.04	0.05	0.09	0.16	0.18	0.21	0.25	0.5
0.3	0.00	0.00	0.01	0.01	0.01	0.02	0.03	0.03	0.05	0.11	0.19	0.27	0.42	0.3
0.2	0.00	0.00	0.00	0.01	0.01	0.01	0.02	0.02	0.04	0.07	0.13	0.27	0.63	0.2
0.1	0.00	0.00	0.00	0.00	0.00	0.01	0.01	0.01	0.01	0.04	0.06	0.14	1.25	0.1

4 EFFECT OF TIMBER DECK CARGO

In the case of ships carrying timber deck cargoes, the Administration may allow account to be taken of the buoyancy of the deck cargo assuming that such cargo has a permeability of 25% of the volume occupied by the cargo. Additional curves of stability may be required if the Administration considers it necessary to investigate the influence of different permeabilities and/or assumed effective height of the deck cargo.

Appendix 2
Standard conditions of loading to be examined

1   LOADING CONDITIONS

The standard loading conditions referred to in 4.2 of the Recommendation are as follows:

1.1   Passenger ship

.1   Ship in the fully loaded departure condition with full stores and fuel and with the full number of passengers with their luggage;

.2   ship in the fully loaded arrival condition, with the full number of passengers and their luggage but with only 10% stores and fuel remaining;

.3   ship without cargo, but with full stores and fuel and the full number of passengers and their luggage;

.4   ship in the same condition as in .3 above but with only 10% stores and fuel remaining.

1.2   Cargo ship

.1   Ship in the fully loaded departure condition, with cargo homogeneously distributed throughout all cargo spaces and with full stores and fuel;

.2   ship in the fully loaded arrival condition with cargo homogeneously distributed throughout all cargo spaces and with 10% stores and fuel remaining;

.3   ship in ballast in the departure condition, without cargo but with full stores and fuel;

.4   ship in ballast in the arrival condition, without cargo and with 10% stores and fuel remaining.

1.3   Cargo ships intended to carry deck cargoes

.1   Ship in the fully loaded departure condition with cargo homogeneously distributed in the holds and with cargo specified in extension and weight on deck, with full stores and fuel;

.2   ship in the fully loaded arrival condition with cargo homogeneously distributed in holds and with a cargo specified in extension and weight on deck, with 10% stores and fuel.

2   ASSUMPTIONS FOR CALCULATING LOADING CONDITIONS

2.1   For fully loaded conditions mentioned in 1.2.1, 1.2.2, 1.3.1 and 1.3.2 of this appendix, if a dry cargo ship has tanks for liquid cargo, the effective deadweight in the loading conditions therein described should be distributed according to two assumptions, i.e. (i) cargo tanks full and (ii) cargo tanks empty.

2.2   In conditions mentioned in 1.1.1 and 1.2.1 of this appendix, it should be assumed that the ship is loaded to its subdivision load line or summer load line or, if intended to carry a timber deck cargo, to the summer timber load line with water ballast tanks empty.

2.3   If in any loading condition water ballast is necessary, additional diagrams should be calculated taking into account the water ballast. Its quantity and disposition should be stated.

2.4   In all cases the cargo in holds is assumed to be fully homogeneous unless this condition is inconsistent with the practical service of the ship.

2.5   In all cases when deck cargo is carried a realistic stowage weight should be assumed and stated, including the height of the cargo.

2.6   Where timber deck cargoes are carried, the amount of cargo and ballast should correspond to the worst service condition in which all the relevant stability criteria in 5 of the Recommendation are met. In the arrival condition it should be assumed that the weight of the deck cargo has increased by 10% due to water absorption.

2.7   When timber deck cargoes are carried and it is anticipated that some formation of ice will take place, an allowance should be made in the arrival condition for the additional weight.

2.8   A weight of 75 kg should be assumed for each passenger except that this value may be reduced to not less than 60 kg where this can be justified. In addition, the weight and distribution of the luggage should be determined by the Administration.

2.9   The height of the centre of gravity for passengers should be assumed equal to:

> **.1**   1.0 m above deck level for passengers standing upright. Account may be taken, if necessary, of camber and sheer of deck;
>
> **.2**   0.30 m above the seat in respect of seated passengers.

2.10   Passengers and luggage should be considered to be in the spaces normally at their disposal, when assessing compliance with the criteria in 5.1.1 to 5.1.4 of the Recommendation.

2.11   Passengers without luggage should be considered as distributed to produce the most unfavourable combination of passenger heeling moment and/or initial metacentric height, which may be obtained in practice, when assessing compliance with the criteria in 5.3.1 and 5.3.2 of the Recommendation, respectively. In this connection it is anticipated that a value higher than four persons per square metre will not be necessary.

Appendix 3
Memorandum to Administrations on an approximate determination of ship's stability by means of the rolling period tests
(for ships up to 70 m in length)

1   Recognizing the desirability of supplying to masters of small ships instructions for a simplified determination of initial stability, attention was given to the rolling period tests. Studies on this matter have now been completed with the result that the rolling period test may be recommended as a useful means of approximately determining the initial stability of small ships when it is not practicable to give approved loading conditions or other stability information, or as a supplement to such information.

2   Investigations comprising the evaluation of a number of inclining and rolling tests according to various formulae showed that the following formula gave the best results, and it has the advantage of being the simplest:

$$GM_0 = \left(\frac{fB}{T_r}\right)^2$$

where:

  f = factor for the rolling period/rolling coefficient (calculated using metric system)

  B = breadth of the ship in metric units

  T_r = time for a full rolling period in seconds (i.e. for one oscillation "to and fro" port–starboard–port, or vice versa).

3   The factor f is of the greatest importance and the data from the above tests were used for assessing the influence of the distribution of the various masses in the whole body of the loaded ship.

4   For coasters of normal size (excluding tankers), the following average values were observed:

  .1   empty ship or ship carrying ballast: $f \sim 0.88$

  .2   ship fully loaded and with liquids in tanks comprising the following percentage of the total load on board (i.e. cargo, liquids, stores, etc.):

20% of total load	$f \sim 0.78$
10% of total load	$f \sim 0.75$
5% of total load	$f \sim 0.73$

  The stated values are mean values. Generally, observed f-values were within ± 0.05 of those given above.

5   These f-values were based upon a series of limited tests and, therefore, Administrations should re-examine these in the light of any different circumstances applying to their own ships.

6 It must be noted that the greater the distance of masses from the rolling axis, the greater the rolling coefficient will be.

Therefore it can be expected that:

- the rolling coefficient for an unloaded ship, i.e. for a hollow body, will be higher than that for a loaded ship;
- the rolling coefficient for a ship carrying a great amount of bunkers and ballast – both groups are usually located in the double bottom, i.e. far away from the rolling axis – will be higher than that of the same ship having an empty double bottom.

7 The above recommended rolling coefficients were determined by tests with vessels in port and with their consumable liquids at normal working levels; thus the influences exerted by the vicinity of the quay, the limited depth of water and the free surfaces of liquids in service tanks are covered.

8 Experiments have shown that the results of the rolling test method get increasingly less reliable the nearer they approach GM–values of 0.20 m and below.

9 For the following reasons, it is not generally recommended that results be obtained from rolling oscillations taken in a seaway:

.1 exact coefficients for tests in open waters are not available;

.2 the rolling periods observed may not be free oscillations but forced oscillations due to seaway;

.3 frequently, oscillations are either irregular or only regular for too short an interval of time to allow accurate measurements to be observed;

.4 specialized recording equipment is necessary.

10 However, sometimes it may be desirable to use the vessel's period of roll as a means of approximately judging the stability at sea. If this is done, care should be taken to discard readings which depart appreciably from the majority of other observations. Forced oscillations corresponding to the sea period and differing from the natural period at which the vessel seems to move should be disregarded. In order to obtain satisfactory results, it may be necessary to select intervals when the sea action is least violent, and it may be necessary to discard a considerable number of observations.

11 In view of the foregoing circumstances, it needs to be recognized that the determination of the stability by means of the rolling test in disturbed waters should only be regarded as a very approximate estimation.

12 The formula given in 2 above can be reduced to:

$$GM_0 = \frac{f}{T_r^2}$$

and the Administration should determine the f-value(s) for each vessel.

13   The determination of the stability can be simplified by giving the master permissible rolling periods, in relation to the draughts, for the appropriate value(s) of f considered necessary.

14   The initial stability may also be more easily determined graphically by using the attached sample nomogram, as described below:

.1   the values for B and f are marked in the relevant scales and connected by a straight line (1). This straight line intersects the vertical line (mm) in the point (M);

.2   a second straight line (2) which connects this point (M) and the point on the T_r scale corresponding with the determined rolling period, intersects the GM scale at the requested value.

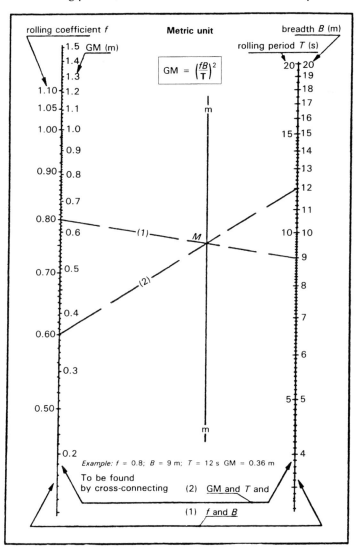

15   The annex to appendix 3 shows an example of a recommended form in which these instructions might be presented by each Administration to the masters. It is considered that each Administration should recommend the *f*-value or values to be used.

Annex to appendix 3
Suggested form of guidance to the master on
an approximate determination of ship's stability
by means of the rolling period test

INTRODUCTION

1   If the following instructions are properly carried out, this method allows a reasonably quick and accurate estimation of the metacentric height, which is a measure of the ship's stability.

2   The method depends upon the relationship between the metacentric height and the rolling period in terms of the extreme breadth of the vessel.

TEST PROCEDURE

3   The rolling period required is the time for one complete oscillation of the vessel and to ensure the most accurate results in obtaining this value the following precautions should be observed:

.1   The test should be conducted with the vessel in harbour, in smooth water with the minimum interference from wind and tide.

.2   Starting with the vessel at the extreme end of a roll to one side (say port) and the vessel about to move towards the upright, one complete oscillation will have been made when the vessel has moved right across to the other extreme side (i.e. starboard) and returned to the original starting point and is about to commence the next roll.

.3   By means of a stop-watch, the time should be taken for not less than about five of these complete oscillations; the counting of these oscillations should begin when the vessel is at the extreme end of a roll. After allowing the roll to completely fade away, this operation should be repeated at least twice more. If possible, in every case the same number of complete oscillations should be timed to establish that the readings are consistent, i.e. repeating themselves within reasonable limits. Knowing the total time for the total number of oscillations made, the mean time for one complete oscillation can be calculated.

.4 The vessel can be made to roll by rhythmically lifting up and putting down a weight as far off the centreline as possible; by pulling on the mast with a rope; by people running athwartships in unison; or by any other means. However, and this is most important, as soon as this forced rolling has commenced the means by which it has been induced must be stopped and the vessel allowed to roll freely and naturally. If rolling has been induced by lowering or raising a weight it is preferable that the weight is moved by a dockside crane. If the ship's own derrick is used, the weight should be placed on the deck, at the centreline, as soon as the rolling is established.

.5 The timing and counting of the oscillations should only begin when it is judged that the vessel is rolling freely and naturally, and only as much as is necessary to accurately count these oscillations.

.6 The mooring should be slack and the vessel "breasted off" to avoid making any contact during its rolling. To check this, and also to get some idea of the number of complete oscillations that can be reasonably counted and timed, a preliminary rolling test should be made before starting to record actual times.

.7 Care should be taken to ensure that there is a reasonable clearance of water under the keel and at the sides of the vessel.

.8 Weights of reasonable size which are liable to swing (e.g. a lifeboat) or liable to move (e.g. a drum) should be secured against such movement. The free surface effects of slack tanks should be kept as small as is practicable during the test and the voyage.

DETERMINATION OF THE INITIAL STABILITY

4 Having calculated the period for one complete oscillation, say T seconds, the metacentric height GM_0 can be calculated from the following formula:

$$GM_0 = \frac{f}{T^2}$$

where f is ... (to be determined for each particular vessel by the Administration).

5 The calculated value of GM_0 should be equal to or greater than the critical value which is ... (to be determined for each particular vessel by the Administration).

LIMITATIONS TO THE USE OF THIS METHOD

6   A long period of roll corresponding to a GM_0 of 0.20 m or below indicates a condition of low stability. However, under such circumstances, accuracy in determination of the actual value of GM_0 is reduced.

7   If, for some reason, these rolling tests are carried out in open, deep, but smooth waters, inducing the roll, for example, by putting over the helm, then the GM_0 calculated by using the method and coefficient of paragraph 3 above should be reduced by ... (figure to be estimated by the Administration) to obtain the final answer.

8   The determination of stability by means of the rolling test in disturbed waters should only be regarded as a very approximate estimation. If such test is performed, care should be taken to discard readings which depart appreciably from the majority of other observations. Forced oscillations corresponding to the sea period and differing from the natural period at which the vessel seems to move should be disregarded. In order to obtain satisfactory results, it may be necessary to select intervals when the sea action is least violent, and it may be necessary to discard a considerable number of observations.

Appendix D

Text of regulation 44 of
the International Convention on Load Lines, 1966*

Regulation 44
Stowage

General

(1)   Openings in the weather deck over which cargo is stowed shall be securely closed and battened down. The ventilators shall be efficiently protected.

(2)   Timber deck cargo shall extend over at least the entire available length which is the total length of the well or wells between superstructures. Where there is no limiting superstructure at the after end, the timber shall extend at least to the after end of the aftermost hatchway. The timber shall be stowed as solidly as possible to at least the standard height of the superstructure.

(3)   On a cargo ship within a seasonal winter zone in winter, the height of the deck cargo above the weather deck shall not exceed one third of the extreme breadth of the ship.

(4)   The timber deck cargo shall be compactly stowed, lashed and secured. It shall not interfere in any way with the navigation and necessary work of the ship.

Uprights

(5)   Uprights, when required by the nature of the timber, shall be of adequate strength considering the breadth of the ship; the spacing shall be suitable for the length and character of timber carried, but shall not exceed 3 m (9.8 ft.). Strong angles or metal sockets or equally efficient means shall be provided for securing the uprights.

Lashings

(6)   Timber deck cargo shall be efficiently secured throughout its length by independent overall lashings spaced not more than 3 m (9.8 ft.) apart. Eye plates for these lashings shall be efficiently attached to the sheer strake or to the deck stringer plate at intervals of not more than 3 m (9.8 ft.). The distance from an end bulkhead

---

* This text remains in force until the entry into force of the Protocol of 1988 relating to the International Convention on Load Lines, 1966 (see note below on page 43).

of a superstructure to the first eye plate shall be not more than 2 m (6.6 ft.). Eye plates and lashings shall be provided 0.6 m (23$^1/_2$ in) and 1.5 m (4.9 ft.) from the ends of timber deck cargoes where there is no bulkhead.

(7)   Lashings shall be not less than 19 mm ($^3/_4$ in) close link chain or flexible wire rope of equivalent strength, fitted with sliphooks and turnbuckles, which shall be accessible at all times. Wire rope lashings shall have a short length of long link chain to permit the length of lashings to be regulated.

(8)   When timber is in lengths less than 3.6 m (11.8 ft.) the spacing of the lashings shall be reduced or other suitable provisions made to suit the length of timber.

(9)   All fittings required for securing the lashings shall be of strength corresponding to the strength of the lashings.

Stability

(10)   Provision shall be made for a safe margin of stability at all stages of the voyage, regard being given to additions of weight, such as those due to absorption of water and icing and to losses of weight such as those due to consumption of fuel and stores.

Protection of crew, access to machinery spaces, etc.

(11)   In addition to the requirements of regulation 25(5) of this annex, guardrails or lifelines spaced not more than 330 mm (13 in) apart vertically shall be provided on each side of the deck cargo to a height of at least 1 m (39$^1/_2$ in) above the cargo.

Steering arrangements

(12)   Steering arrangements shall be effectively protected from damage by cargo and, as far as practicable, shall be accessible. Efficient provision shall be made for steering in the event of a breakdown in the main steering arrangements.

Note: Upon the entry into force of the Protocol of 1988 relating to the International Convention on Load Lines, 1966,* the text of regulation 44 will be replaced by the following:

Regulation 44
Stowage

General

(1)   Openings in the weather deck over which cargo is stowed shall be securely closed and battened down.

The ventilators and air pipes shall be efficiently protected.

(2)   Timber deck cargoes shall extend over at least the entire available length which is the total length of the well or wells between superstructures.

Where there is no limiting superstructure at the after end, the timber shall extend at least to the after end of the aftermost hatchway.

The timber deck cargo shall extend athwartships as close as possible to the ship's side, due allowance being made for obstructions such as guardrails, bulwark stays, uprights, pilot access, etc., provided any gap thus created at the side of the ship shall not exceed a mean of 4% of the breadth. The timber shall be stowed as solidly as possible to at least the standard height of the superstructure other than any raised quarterdeck.

(3)   On a ship within a seasonal winter zone in winter, the height of the deck cargo above the weather deck shall not exceed one third of the extreme breadth of the ship.

(4)   The timber deck cargo shall be compactly stowed, lashed and secured. It shall not interfere in any way with the navigation and necessary work of the ship.

---

* Article V of the Protocol (entry into force) states, in part, as follows:

"1   The present Protocol shall enter into force twelve months after the date on which both the following conditions have been met:
  (a)   not less than fifteen States, the combined merchant fleets of which constitute not less than fifty per cent of the gross tonnage of the world's merchant shipping, have expressed their consent to be bound by it in accordance with article IV, and
  (b)   the conditions for the entry into force of the Protocol of 1988 relating to the International Convention for the Safety of Life at Sea, 1974, have been met,
provided that the present Protocol shall not enter into force before 1 February 1992."

Uprights

(5)   Uprights, when required by the nature of the timber, shall be of adequate strength considering the breadth of the ship; the strength of the uprights shall not exceed the strength of the bulkwark and the spacing shall be suitable for the length and character of timber carried, but shall not exceed 3 m. Strong angles or metal sockets or equally efficient means shall be provided for securing the uprights.

Lashings

(6)   Timber deck cargo shall be effectively secured throughout its length by a lashing system acceptable to the Administration for the character of the timber carried.

Stability

(7)   Provision shall be made for a safe margin of stability at all stages of the voyage, regard being given to additions of weight, such as those arising from absorption of water or icing, if applicable, and to losses of weight such as those arising from consumption of fuel and stores.

Resolution A.715(17)
Adopted on 6 November 1991

THE ASSEMBLY,

RECALLING Article 15(j) of the Convention on the International Maritime Organization concerning the functions of the Assembly in relation to regulations and guidelines concerning maritime safety,

RECALLING FURTHER that, by resolution A.287(VIII), it had adopted the Code of Safe Practice for Ships Carrying Timber Deck Cargoes, which was subsequently amended by the Maritime Safety Committee at its thirty-ninth session in 1978,

RECOGNIZING the need to improve the provisions contained in the Code in the light of experience gained,

HAVING CONSIDERED the recommendations made by the Maritime Safety Committee at its fifty-eighth session,

1.   ADOPTS the Code of Safe Practice for Ships Carrying Timber Deck Cargoes, 1991, set out in the annex* to the present resolution;

2.   RECOMMENDS Governments to apply the 1991 Code in lieu of the Code annexed to resolution A.287(VIII), as amended in 1978;

3.   INVITES the Maritime Safety Committee to review appendix D to the Code after the Protocol of 1988 to the International Convention on Load Lines, 1966, enters into force;

4.   REVOKES resolution A.287(VIII).

---

* See page 1.

MLD7

CODE OF SAFE PRACTICE
FOR SHIPS CARRYING
TIMBER DECK
CARGOES, 1991

AL

N

London, 1992

First published in 1974
by the INTERNATIONAL MARITIME ORGANIZATION
4 Albert Embankment, London SE1 7SR

Second edition 1981
Third edition 1992

Printed in the United Kingdom by Ashford Overload Services Ltd.

12   14   16   18   20   19   17   15   13   11

ISBN 92-801-1285-6

IMO PUBLICATION
Sales number: I275E